Phonics Practice

A LAUGHING LOBSTER BOOK 978-1-913906-04-7

Published in Great Britain by Laughing Lobster
an imprint of Centum Publishing Ltd.
This edition published 2021.
1 3 5 7 9 10 8 6 4 2

Illustrations by Louise Gardner.

Laughing Lobster an imprint of Centum Publishing Ltd, 20 Devon Square,
Newton Abbot, Devon, TQ12 2HR, UK
books@centumpublishingltd.co.uk
LAUGHING LOBSTER AN IMPRINT OF CENTUM PUBLISHING
Limited Reg. No. 08497203

A CIP catalogue record for this book is available from the British Library.

Printed in China.

Answers are at the back of the book!

About this book

The activities in this book will help your child to learn about phonics – the building blocks for learning to read and write.

Phonemes

There are 26 letters of the alphabet but they make 44 sounds. These letter sounds are called phonemes.

We teach the children to read letters or groups of letters by saying the sound(s) they represent. Children can then start to read by blending the phonemes together to make words.

For example the word 'bed' is made up of 3 phonemes: b-e-d. Ask your child to sound out each letter sound before they blend them together to say the word.

Enjoy doing the fun activities in this book with your child. Make sure you have plenty of coloured pencils to get started, and try to extend each activity by asking questions, for example:

- Can you find any objects in your bedroom with these phonemes in them?

- Can you write them down?

- Can you draw a picture?

Always give your child plenty of praise and encouragement.

Alphabet letter sounds

Draw a line to match each letter sound to the right picture.

a

b

c

d

e

f

g

h

girl

elephant

cat

ball

fish

dog

apple

hen

Alphabet letter sounds

Draw a line to match each letter sound to the right picture.

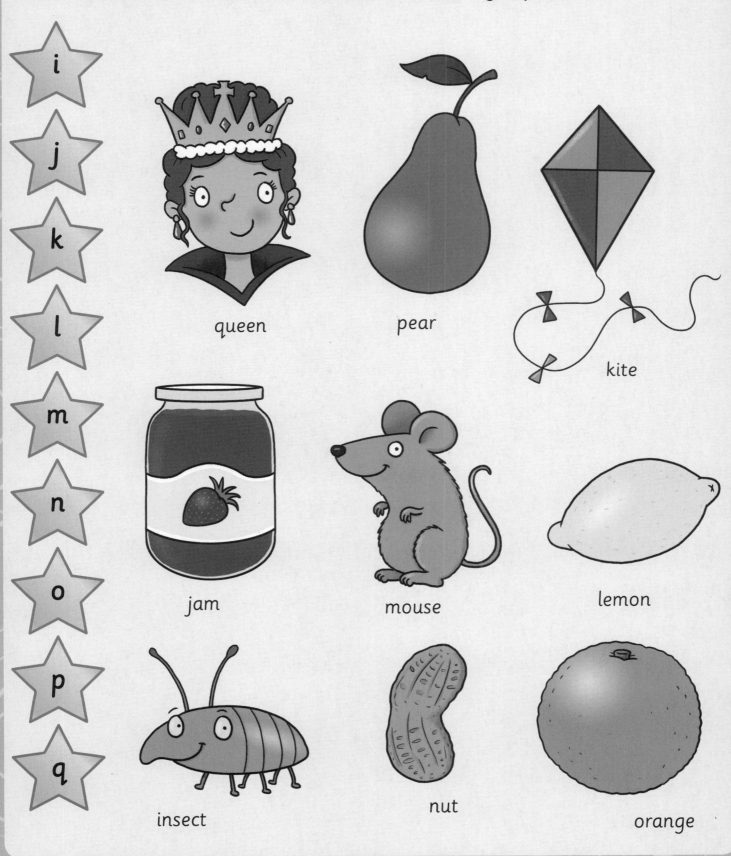

i
j
k
l
m
n
o
p
q

queen

pear

kite

jam

mouse

lemon

insect

nut

orange

Alphabet letter sounds

Draw a line to match each letter sound to the right picture.

umbrella

violin

teddy

rabbit

x-ray

yacht

window

zebra

sock

r
s
t
u
v
w
x
y
z

a, ai, ar, air phonemes

Hello, I'm Joe. Come and learn these phonemes with me.

Now let's have some fun! Draw a picture of an **a**nt and a ch**air** on a f**ar**m in the r**ai**n. Now colour it in.

a
a-n-t
ant

ai
r-ai-n
rain

ar
f-ar-m
farm

air
ch-air
chair

b, d, f, g phonemes

Hello, my name is Mia. Can you say these phonemes out loud with me? Then slowly blend them together to make the words.

b	**d**	**f**	**g**
b-a-t	**d**-o-g	f-o-x	**g**-a-t-e
bat	dog	fox	gate
r-a-**bb**-it	m-u-**dd**-y	f-i-sh	**gu**-i-t-a-r
rabbit	muddy	fish	guitar

rabbit

dog

Now find the words in the grid below. Blend the sounds together as you find each word, then draw a circle round it.

muddy

x	f	r	r	y	o	o	v	i
b	k	p	a	o	s	k	h	y
f	a	s	b	z	o	d	o	g
m	o	t	b	i	s	r	t	f
t	m	k	i	g	p	p	o	i
g	u	i	t	a	r	k	w	s
u	d	p	r	t	q	i	o	h
i	d	j	r	e	d	i	p	o
a	y	s	f	o	x	w	e	r
t	r	s	q	i	y	l	t	w

bat

fox

guitar

fish

gate

e, ee, ear phonemes

Hi, my name is Poppy. Sing out these phonemes with me, then blend them together to make the different words.

ee
f-**ee**-t – feet
s-**ea** – sea
b-**ee** – bee

e
e-g-g – egg
h-**ea**-d – head
f-r-**ie**-n-d – friend

ear
h-**ere** – here
d-**eer** – deer
b-**ear**-d – beard

Write '**ee**', '**e**' or '**ear**' in the spaces to finish these words.

f_ _ _ t

h_ _ n

_ gg

d_ _ _ _ _

s_ _ a

h, i, igh phonemes

I love colouring and painting. Practise these phonemes with me, and then use your pencils to help me finish colouring the pictures on this page.

h
h-e-n – hen
wh-o – who
H-a-r-r-y – Harry

i
i-f – if
w-**o**-m-e-n – women
I-z-z-y – Izzy

igh
n-**igh**-t – night
eyes – eyes

Harry

Mia

Izzy

Choose different colours for all the **eyes**.

Put different patterns on all the **ties**.

Phoneme match

Draw lines to match each phoneme to the right picture.

h

i

igh

tie

Izzy

hen

hat

light

Harry

igloo

knight

j, k, kw phonemes

I'm Mr Gupta, the teacher. Let's practise these phonemes together by saying the sounds out loud. Then blend them together to make the words.

j
j-a-r – jar
b-a-d-**ge** – badge

k
c-a-t – cat
s-**ch**-o-o-l – school

kw
qu-e-s-t-i-o-n – question
qu-e-e-n – queen

Colour in the **c**at **qu**ickly.

Colour the big **qu**estion mark in your favourite colour.

Draw a picture of a **qu**een wearing a **c**rown.

11

j, k, kw phonemes

Use the letters here to fill in the spaces in the words below.

g   ck   j   c   ge   qu

__ar

__ow

gara___ ___

du___ ___

__iant

___ ___een

j, k, kw phonemes

Draw a picture of each word. Then see if you can spot the odd one out in each group of words.

Which word doesn't use the j phoneme?

jar	jelly	gate

Which word doesn't use the k phoneme?

duck	cat	dog

Which word doesn't use the kw phoneme?

queen	quilt	king

l, m phonemes

These groups show the two different phonemes. Draw a circle around the pictures that use the phoneme in the word.

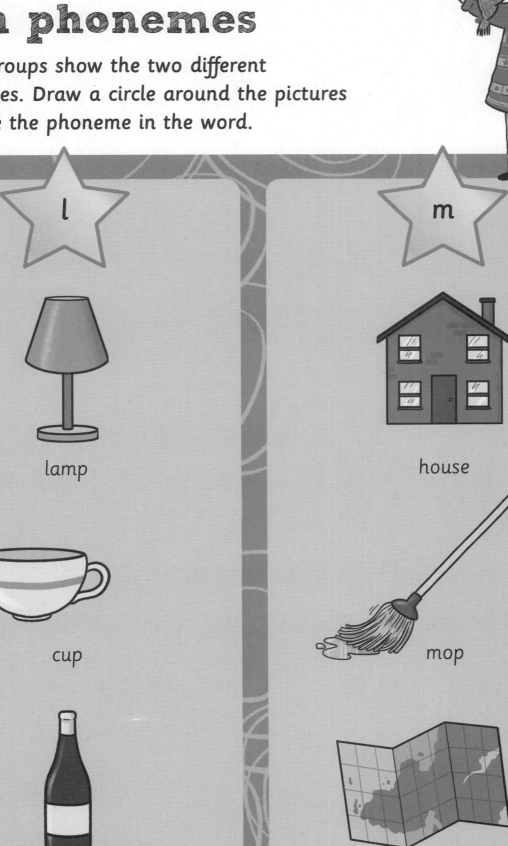

l

lamp

cup

bottle

m

house

mop

map

n, ng phonemes

These groups show the two different phonemes.
Put a tick in the circle next to the pictures that
use the phoneme in the word.

n

knock

baby

nose

ng

sing

wing

cow

o, oa, oo (long), oo (short), phonemes

Say these phonemes out loud with me, then blend them together to make the different words.

o
o-c-t-o-p-u-s —
octopus

oa
c-**oa**-t — coat

oo
(short sound)
b-**oo**-k — book

oo
(long sound)
b-**oo**-t — boot

Draw a picture of an **o**ctopus, a c**oa**t, a b**oo**t and a b**oo**k. Say the sound out loud as you draw each one, then write the words under the pictures.

or, oi, ow phonemes

Now practise these phonemes with me. Say the phonemes out loud, then blend the sounds together to make the different words.

ow
ow-l – owl

or
d-oor – door

oi
c-oi-n – coin

Draw a picture of a **doo**r, a **coi**n and an **ow**l. Say the sounds out loud as you draw each one, then write the words under the pictures.

o, oa, oo (long), oo (short), or, oi, ow phonemes

There are lots of things to help us learn and play in our classroom. Practise these phonemes with us by playing this spotting game.

Can you spot these things in the picture?
Colour in a star every time you find one.

1. a. **dog**   b. **juice**   c. **floor**   d. **boot**   e. **boy**

2. Something beginning with '**b**' that contains fruit.

3. Something in a vase that begins with '**f**'.

4. A toy that has the '**ow**' sound in the word.

5. A number that has the '**oo**' (long) sound in the word.

Let's spot phonemes

Draw a circle around the picture that has the long 'oo' sound.

Put a tick next to the picture that has the short 'oo' sound.

igloo

books

cup

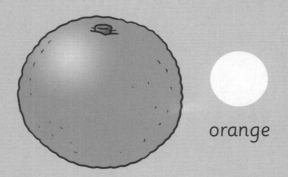

orange

cow

food

p, r, s, t phonemes

Let's say these phonemes together.
They can all be found in different words for food.

p
p-e-a-r — pear
p-o-t-a-t-o — potato

s
s-a-u-s-a-g-e — sausage
s-w-ee-t-s — sweets

t
t-o-a-s-t — toast
b-u-tt-e-r — butter

r
r-ai-s-i-n — raisin
c-a-rr-o-t — carrot

The 'r' phoneme can be found at the beginning
of 'rabbit' and in the middle of 'carrot'.

Draw a line under the 'r' phonemes in the sentence below, then draw
a picture of a carrot.

Can I have a juicy carrot for the rabbit to eat?

p, r, s, t wordsearch

Can you find the words in the grid below?
Blend the sounds together as you find each word,
then draw a circle round it.

sun

pear

carrot

x	f	r	r	y	s	o	c	k
b	t	a	a	o	s	k	h	y
f	a	b	b	z	o	d	o	g
m	b	b	b	t	e	d	d	y
t	l	i	i	g	p	p	o	i
g	e	t	t	a	r	k	w	s
s	f	n	r	t	q	i	o	h
c	a	r	r	o	t	i	p	o
a	y	s	u	n	x	w	e	r
p	o	p	p	y	p	e	a	r

sock

rabbit

Poppy

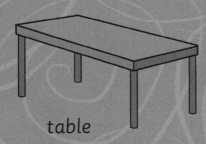

table

teddy

u, ur phonemes

Here are some more phonemes for you to practise.
Start by saying each sound out loud.

u
u-m-b-r-e-l-l-a
– umbrella
s-**u**-n – sun

ur
g-**ir**-l – girl
w-**or**-m – worm

Read the sentence below.

Draw a red line under the 'u' phoneme and a blue line
under the 'ur' phoneme. Then draw a picture to go with it.

The girl saw the worm under an umbrella.

v, w phonemes

Here are some more phonemes for you to practise.
Start by saying each sound out loud.

v

v-a-n — van
v-i-o-l-i-n — violin

w

w-i-n-d-o-w — window
p-e-n-g-**ui**-n — penguin

Read the sentence below.

Draw a red line under the '**v**' phoneme and a blue line under
the '**w**' phoneme. Then draw a picture to go with it.

The penguin sat by the window in the van.

u, ur, v, w phonemes

Use your pencil to trace over the letters.
Say the sounds out loud as you trace the phonemes.

sun

umbrella

violin

van

girl

worm

window

penguin

schwa phoneme

There is another phoneme similar to a 'u' letter sound. It is represented by these letters – 'schwa'. The following words are examples of this sound:

corner, motor, favour, famous, centre

Colour the balloons with words that use the 'schwa' sound in your favourite colour.

flavour

party

centre

crayon

famous

doctor

hand

y, y(oo), y(ure), z, zh phonemes

Try out these sounds with me. Then follow the wiggly lines to match each child to a phoneme in the puzzle below.

y(oo)
n-**ew**-s — news
u-n-i-f-o-r-m — uniform

y
y-e-s — yes
o-n-**i**-o-n — onion

zh
v-i-**si**-o-n — vision
b-e-i-**ge** — beige

y(ure)
p-**ure** — pure
c-**ure** — cure

z
z-i-p — zip
x-y-l-o-p-h-o-n-e — xylophone

Write the matching phoneme in the box below each child. Blend the sounds together to read the word.

ze   ee   r   b

Then use the word you've made to complete this sentence:

We fly our kite when there's a good b_____.

y, y(oo), y(ure), z, zh phonemes

Colour the balloons that contain the 'y' (oo) sound in pink, and the 'y' (ure) sound in yellow. Colour the 'z' sound in red, the 'zh' sound in blue and the 'y' sound in purple.

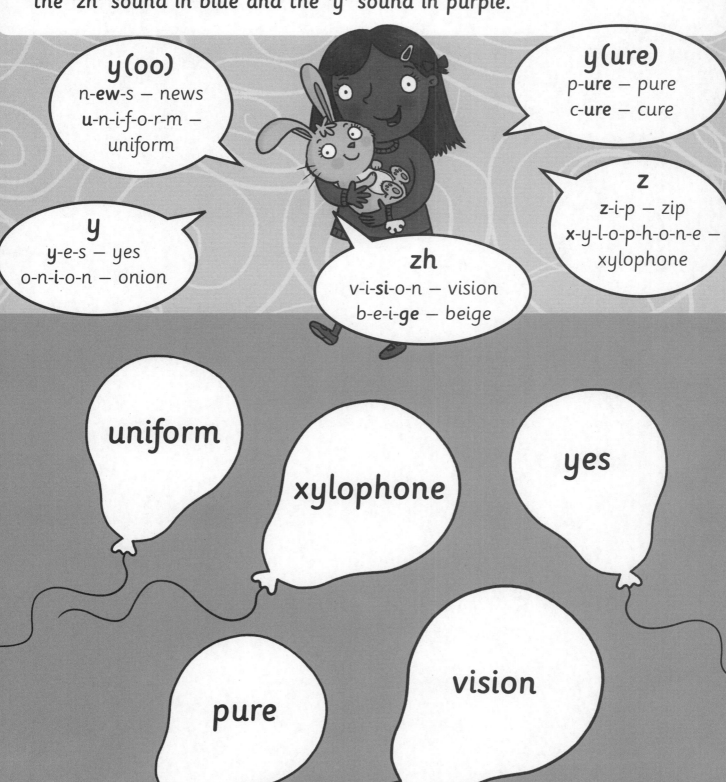

y(oo)
n-**ew**-s — news
u-n-i-f-o-r-m — uniform

y(ure)
p-**ure** — pure
c-**ure** — cure

z
z-i-p — zip
x-y-l-o-p-h-o-n-e — xylophone

y
y-e-s — yes
o-n-**i**-o-n — onion

zh
v-i-**si**-o-n — vision
b-e-i-**ge** — beige

uniform

xylophone

yes

pure

vision

gz, ks phonemes

These phonemes are quite difficult to say, but if you practise you'll soon get the hang of them. Each sound is usually represented by the letter 'x'.

gz
e-x-a-m —
exam

ks
f-o-x — fox

'gz' or 'ks' phoneme?

Say each word and write the correct phoneme by each one.

 box

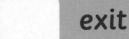 exit

 six

 ox

example

ch, sh, th phonemes

What fun phonemes! Say them out loud, then blend them together to make the words.

ch
ch-e-e-s-e — cheese

th
th-u-m-b — thumb

sh
sh-e-e-p — sheep

Write the 'ch' or 'sh' or 'th' phonemes to finish these words.

___ air

fi___

mat___

13

___irteen

___ oes

ba___

Answers

Page 3

a
b
c
d
e
f
g
h

girl
elephant
cat
ball
fish
dog
apple
hen

Page 4

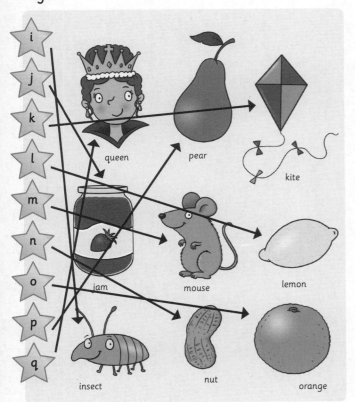

i
j
k
l
m
n
o
p
q

queen
pear
kite
jam
mouse
lemon
insect
nut
orange

Page 5

r
s
t
u
v
w
x
y
z

umbrella
violin
teddy
rabbit
window
yacht
x-ray
zebra
sock

Page 7

x	f	r	r	y	o	o	v	i
b	k	p	a	o	s	k	h	y
f	a	s	b	z	o	d	o	g
m	o	t	b	i	s	r	t	f
t	m	k	i	g	p	p	o	i
g	u	i	t	a	r	k	w	s
u	d	p	r	t	q	i	o	h
i	d	j	r	e	d	i	p	o
a	y	s	f	o	x	w	e	r
t	r	s	q	i	y	l	t	w

Page 8
feet, hen, egg, deer, sea

30

Answers

Page 10

Page 12
jar, **c**ow, gara**ge**, du**ck**, **g**iant, **qu**een

Page 13
gate, dog, king

Page 14

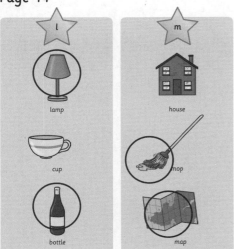

Page 15

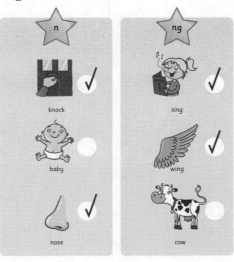

Page 18

2. '**b**' – bowl   3. '**f**' – flowers
4. '**ow**' – clown   5. '**oo**' – two

Page 19
long '**oo**' = food
short '**oo**' = books

Page 20

Can I have a juicy ca**rr**ot for the <u>r</u>abbit to eat?

Page 21

x	f	r	r	y	s	o	c	k
b	t	a	a	o	s	k	h	y
f	a	b	b	z	o	d	q	g
m	b	b	b	t	e	d	d	y
t	l	i	i	g	p	p	o	i
g	e	t	t	a	r	k	w	s
s	f	n	r	t	q	i	o	h
c	a	r	r	o	t	i	p	o
a	y	s	u	n	x	w	e	r
p	o	p	p	y	p	e	a	r

Answers

Page 22

The g<u>ir</u>l saw the w<u>or</u>m <u>u</u>nder an <u>u</u>mbrella.

Page 23

The peng<u>ui</u>n sat by the w<u>i</u>ndow in the v<u>a</u>n.

Page 25

schwa = flavour, centre, doctor, famous

Page 26

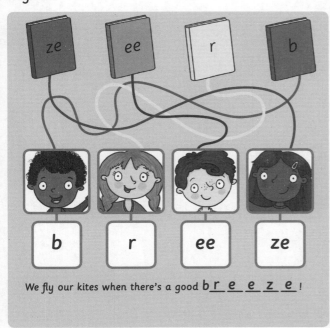

We fly our kites when there's a good b r e e z e !

Page 27

pink = uniform
red = xylophone
green = yes

yellow = pure
blue = vision

Page 28

ks – box, **gz** – exit,
ks – six, **ks** – ox, **gz** – example

Page 29

chair, fi**sh**, mat**ch**, **th**irteen, **sh**oes, ba**th**